- Matched to National Curriculum tests
- 400 practice questions
- Develops essential number skills for speed and accuracy

with over 100 reward stickers

Published 2016 by Bloomsbury Publishing Plc
50 Bedford Square, London, WC1B 3DP

www.bloomsbury.com

Bloomsbury is a registered trademark of Bloomsbury Publishing Plc

ISBN 978-1-4729-2372-1

First published 2016

A CIP catalogue for this book is available from the British Library.

10 9 8 7 6 5 4 3 2 1

Printed in China by Leo Paper Products

This book is produced using paper that is made from wood grown in managed, sustainable forests. It is natural, renewable and recyclable. The logging and manufacturing process conform to the environmental regulations of the country of origin.

To see our full range of titles visit **www.bloomsbury.com**

B L O O M S B U R Y

INTRODUCTION

This is the fifth in the series of Andrew Brodie *Let's Do Arithmetic* books. The book contains 400 arithmetic questions, deliberately designed to cover the following key aspects of the 'Number' section of the National Curriculum:

- Number and place value
- Addition and subtraction
- Multiplication and division
- Fractions

This book has been specifically written to match the updated National Curriculum tests, in which an arithmetic paper replaces the old mental maths tests. The paper consists of 35–40 questions that range from basic addition and subtraction to calculations with fractions at Key Stage 2. Your child will have 30 minutes to complete the test, so it will be useful for them to practise against the clock.

Your child will benefit most greatly if you have the opportunity to discuss the questions with them. You may find that your child gains low scores when they first begin to take the tests. Make sure that they don't lose confidence. Instead, encourage them to learn from their mistakes.

The level of difficulty increases gradually throughout the book, but note that some questions are repeated. This is to ensure that pupils learn vital new facts: they may not know the answer to a particular question the first time they encounter it, but this provides the opportunity for you to help them to learn it for the next time that they come across it. Don't be surprised if they need to practise certain questions lots of times.

It can be helpful to put up posters on the bedroom wall, showing facts such as the multiplication tables. In Year 5, pupils are encouraged to revise their knowledge of all tables up to 12 x 12 and to use these when completing short and long multiplication questions and short division questions. They also learn about square numbers and cube numbers.

TALK ABOUT FRACTIONS:

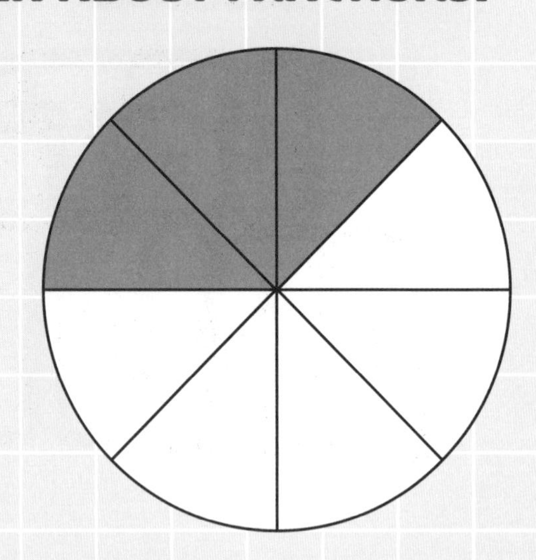

Explain that the circle is cut into 8 pieces so we are dealing with eighths; 3 of these are shaded, so the fraction shaded is three eighths. We write one eighth like this: $\frac{1}{8}$, and we show three eighths like this: $\frac{3}{8}$. In Year 5, pupils add and subtract fractions, and convert mixed numbers to improper fractions and vice versa.

Children gain confidence by learning facts that they can use in their work. With lots of practice they will see their score improve and will learn to find maths both satisfying and enjoyable.

1. 79 + 6 = ☐

2. 92 – 8 = ☐

3. 3725 + 200 = ☐

4. 6559 – 300 = ☐

5.

	6	4	8
+	3	3	1

6.

	8	9	6
–	3	4	5

7. 16 + 5 = 10 + ☐

8. 36 = 4 x ☐

9. 54 ÷ 6 = ☐

10. Round 4646 to the nearest ten. ☐

"Are you quick at adding and subtracting?"

TEST 2

1. 84 + 9 = ☐

2. 73 – 6 = ☐

3. 4695 + 700 = ☐

4. 8748 – 600 = ☐

5.

	5	7	2
+	2	1	8

6.

	7	5	4
–	4	7	7

7. 27 + 6 = 10 + ☐

8. 48 = 4 x ☐

9. 72 ÷ 8 = ☐

10. Round 5113 to the nearest ten. ☐

"Read the questions carefully."

TEST 3

1. $123 + 8 =$ ☐

2. $144 - 6 =$ ☐

3. $5237 + 800 =$ ☐

4. $9124 - 1000 =$ ☐

5. $$\begin{array}{r} 859 \\ +\ 367 \\ \hline \end{array}$$

6. $$\begin{array}{r} 942 \\ -\ 381 \\ \hline \end{array}$$

7. $15 + 8 = 10 +$ ☐

8. $32 = 4 \times$ ☐

9. $96 \div 8 =$ ☐

10. Round 18642 to the nearest ten. ☐

"Adding hundreds changes the hundreds digit and can change the thousands as well."

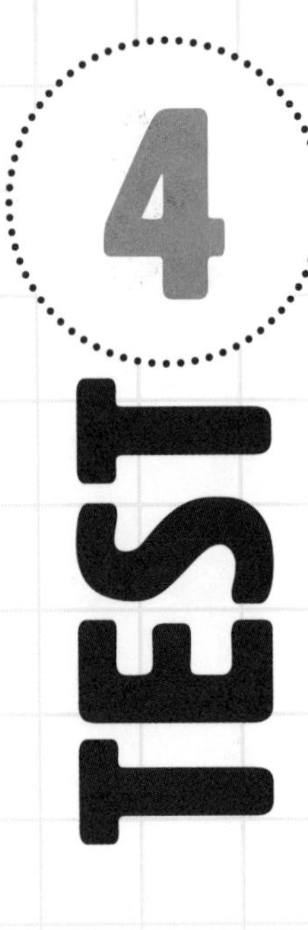

1. $144 + 8 =$ ☐

2. $183 - 6 =$ ☐

3. $6192 + 900 =$ ☐

4. $8431 - 2000 =$ ☐

5.
$$\begin{array}{r} 978 \\ +\ 295 \\ \hline \end{array}$$

6.
$$\begin{array}{r} 873 \\ -\ 242 \\ \hline \end{array}$$

7. $17 + 8 = 9 +$ ☐

8. $35 = 5 \times$ ☐

9. $64 \div 8 =$ ☐

10. Round 25599 to the nearest ten. ☐

"Subtracting hundreds changes the hundreds digit and can change the thousands too."

TEST

1 175 + 8 = ☐

2 195 – 6 = ☐

3 5734 + 800 = ☐

4 6274 – 800 = ☐

5
$$\begin{array}{r} 7\ 3\ 9 \\ +\ 4\ 8\ 8 \\ \hline \\ \hline \end{array}$$

6
$$\begin{array}{r} 9\ 0\ 0 \\ -\ 3\ 5\ 7 \\ \hline \\ \hline \end{array}$$

7 16 + 9 = 7 + ☐

8 56 = 8 x ☐

9 40 ÷ 8 = ☐

10 Round 40017 to the nearest ten. ☐

"Look at question 7: both sides of the equals sign must be worth the same."

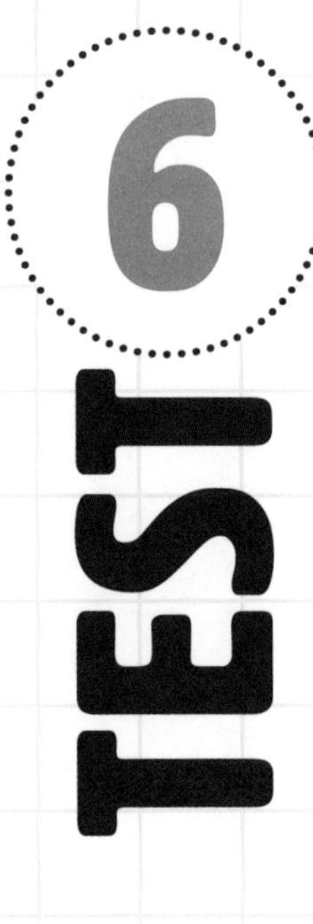

"Do you know the squares of all the numbers from 1 to 12?"

1. 472 + 8 =

2. 256 − 6 =

3. 6935 + 200 =

4. 8427 − 600 =

5.
```
  1 6 4 3
+   2 9 7
---------
```

6.
```
  1 5 6 0
−   4 4 8
---------
```

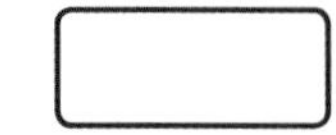

7. 4^2 =

8.
```
  4 3
x   3
-----
```

9. 108 ÷ 9 =

10. Round 6492 to the nearest hundred.

TEST 7

1. 742 + 8 =

2. 571 – 6 =

3. 8493 + 600 =

4. 9397 – 700 =

5.
```
   5 4 7 2
+    4 7 8
```

6.
```
   1 6 0 0
–    5 1 2
```

7. 5^2 =

8.
```
   2 9
x    3
```

9. 81 ÷ 9 =

10. Round 3456 to the nearest hundred.

"Do you know all your multiplication tables?"

TEST 8

1. 361 + 9 = 

2. 493 – 7 = 

3. 9904 + 700 =

4. 1000 – 250 =

5.
```
    6 3 4 2
+   1 5 7 9
-----------
```

6.
```
    2 8 4 2
–   1 6 9 7
-----------
```

7. $6^2 =$

8.
```
    4 8
x     4
-------
```

9. 63 ÷ 9 =

10. Round 12315 to the nearest hundred.

"You might like to use the column addition method for question 3."

TEST 9

1. $412 + 9 =$ ☐

2. $684 - 7 =$ ☐

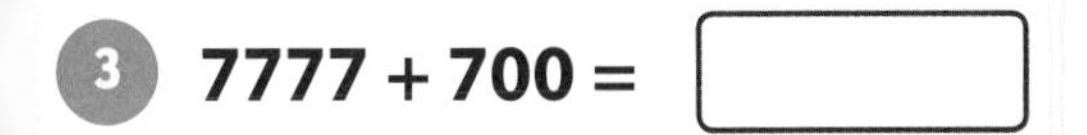

3. $7777 + 700 =$ ☐

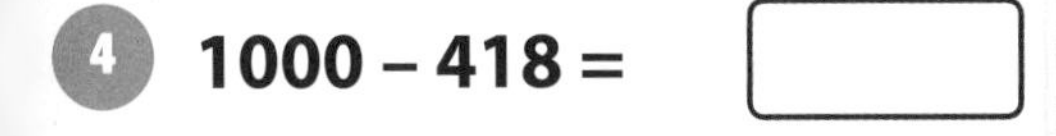

4. $1000 - 418 =$ ☐

5.

	8	9	3	5
+	2	7	8	4

6.

	6	0	3	2
–	2	7	9	4

7. $7^2 =$ ☐

8.

	5	6
x		4

9. $54 \div 9 =$ ☐

10. Round 17698 to the nearest hundred. ☐

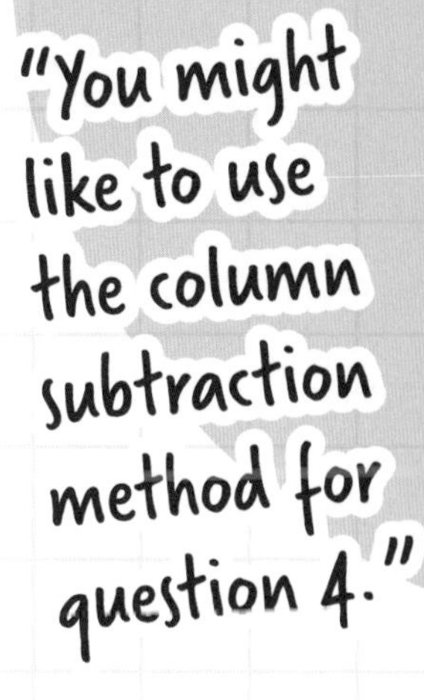

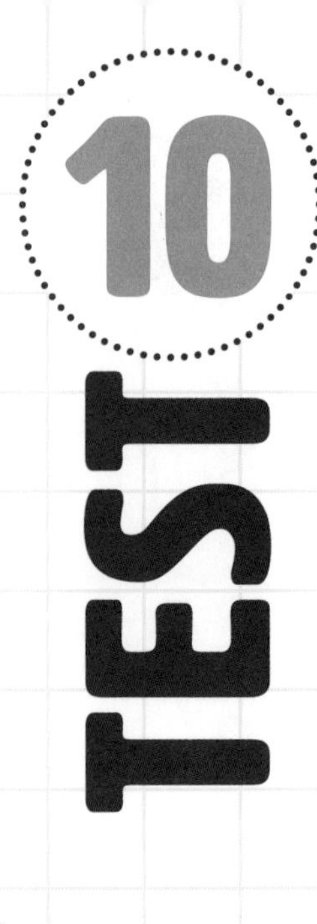

1. 533 + 9 = ☐

2. 755 – 7 = ☐

3. 8564 + 600 = ☐

4. 1000 – 193 = ☐

5.
```
    7 6 2 9
  + 3 5 8 2
  ---------
```

"You might like to use the column subtraction method for question 4."

6.
```
    5 1 3 6
  – 3 9 2 4
  ---------
```

7. 8^2 = ☐

8.
```
      7 8
  x     4
  -------
```

9. 45 ÷ 9 = ☐

10. Round 47688 to the nearest hundred. ☐

TOTAL SCORE

TEST 11

1. 624 + 9 = ☐

2. 966 – 7 = ☐

3. 5920 + 700 = ☐

4. 1000 – 623 = ☐

5.

	9	2	7	8
+	8	0	4	7

6.

	7	3	4	2
–	5	8	4	7

7. 9^2 = ☐

8.

	8	6
x		4

9. 36 ÷ 9 = ☐

10. Round 207198 to the nearest hundred. ☐

REWARD STICKER!

"Be careful when you subtract from 1000."

TEST 12

1. 105 + 9 =

2. 842 – 12 =

3. 12347 + 500 =

4. 1000 – 212 =

5.
$$\begin{array}{r} 14678 \\ +\ \ 2947 \\ \hline \end{array}$$

6.
$$\begin{array}{r} 8010 \\ -\ 3629 \\ \hline \end{array}$$

7. 1^2 =

8.
$$\begin{array}{r} 48 \\ \times\ \ 7 \\ \hline \end{array}$$

9. 32 ÷ 8 =

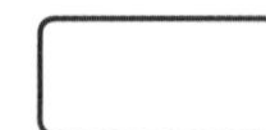

10. Round 207198 to the nearest thousand.

“Think carefully about the answer to question 7.”

13 TEST

1. 666 + 9 = ☐

2. 674 – 14 = ☐

3. 15384 + 900 = ☐

4. 1000 – 622 = ☐

5.

	3	6	7	4	3
+		5	6	0	9

6.

	9	0	0	0
–	4	8	4	2

7. 10^2 = ☐

8.

	5	3
x		7

9. 48 ÷ 8 = ☐

10. Round 345290 to the nearest thousand. ☐

"Do you know the name of every column in question 5?"

TEST 14

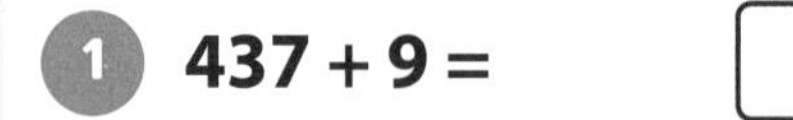

1. 437 + 9 =

2. 839 – 19 =

3. 23602 + 300 =

4. 1000 – 795 =

5.
```
    4 8 3 4 9
  +   7 5 9 9
  -----------
```

6.
```
    8 0 0 0
  – 3 4 2 8
  ---------
```

7. 11^2 =

8.
```
    8 9
  x   7
  -----
```

9. 56 ÷ 8 =

10. Round 764800 to the nearest thousand.

"How quickly can you complete this test?"

TEST 15

1. 768 + 9 =

2. 595 – 15 =

3. 18798 + 600 =

4. 1000 – 47 =

5.
	6	7	3	4	2
+		8	0	9	1

6.
	7	0	0	0
–	1	7	6	4

7. 12^2 =

8.
	6	5
x		7

9. 64 ÷ 8 =

10. Round 300604 to the nearest thousand.

"Do you know what a square root is? The square root of 64 is 8."

REWARD STICKER!

1. $999 + 9 =$ ☐

2. $426 - 16 =$ ☐

3. $46729 + 200 =$ ☐

4. $1000 - 675 =$ ☐

5.

	1	6	7	8	4
+		9	4	7	2

6.

	1	6	7	8	4
–		9	4	7	2

7. $1^3 =$ ☐

8.

	2	4	6
x			2

9. $96 \div 8 =$ ☐

10. Round 247782 to the nearest thousand. ☐

"Question 7 has a surprising answer!"

TEST 17

1. $460 + 12 =$ ☐

2. $818 - 18 =$ ☐

3. $\frac{1}{5} + \frac{2}{5} =$ ☐

4. $1000 - 319 =$ ☐

5.
$$\begin{array}{r} 47341 \\ +\ 17063 \\ \hline \end{array}$$

6.
$$\begin{array}{r} 47294 \\ -\ 8563 \\ \hline \end{array}$$

7. $2^3 =$ ☐

8.
$$\begin{array}{r} 367 \\ \times\ 2 \\ \hline \end{array}$$

9. $49 \div 7 =$ ☐

10. Round 47782 to the nearest ten thousand. ☐

"2^3 means $2 \times 2 \times 2$."

TEST 18

1. 580 + 13 =  

2. 647 – 17 =

3. $\frac{1}{6} + \frac{1}{6} =$ 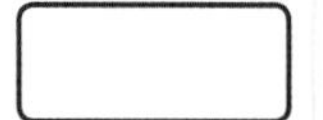

4. 1000 – 150 = 

5.

	7	8	0	1	9
+	1	5	2	3	4

6.

	6	3	7	8	2
–	2	3	6	1	5

7. $3^3 =$ 

8.

	4	7	9
x			2

9. 63 ÷ 7 =

10. Round 84900 to the nearest ten thousand.

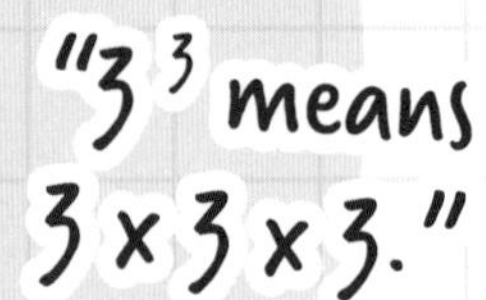

TEST 19

1. $620 + 19 =$ ☐

2. $934 - 14 =$ ☐

3. $\frac{1}{8} + \frac{3}{8} =$ 

4. $1000 - 742 =$ ☐

5. $$\begin{array}{r} 47295 \\ +\ 23976 \\ \hline \end{array}$$

6. $$\begin{array}{r} 84328 \\ -\ 35613 \\ \hline \end{array}$$

7. $4^3 =$ ☐

8. $$\begin{array}{r} 859 \\ \times\ 2 \\ \hline \end{array}$$

9. $84 \div 7 =$ ☐

10. Round 67298 to the nearest ten thousand. ☐

"4^3 means $4 \times 4 \times 4$."

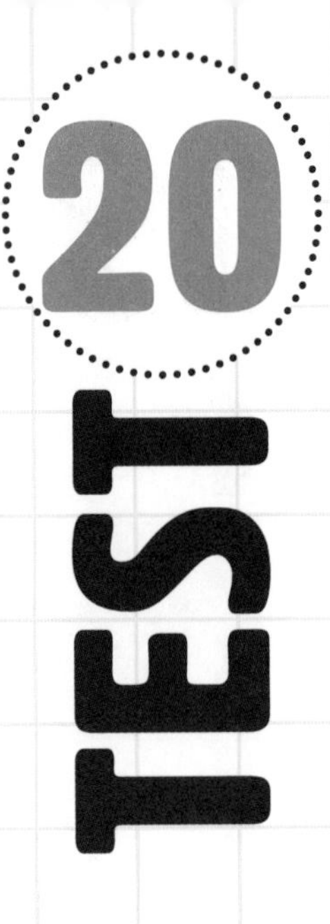

1. $790 + 11 =$

2. $467 - 17 =$

3. $\frac{1}{8} + \frac{5}{8} =$

4. $2000 - 750 =$

"Can you guess what 5^3 means?"

5.

	8	9	3	2	6
+	3	7	4	5	6

6.

	9	2	7	3	4
–	8	7	6	3	9

7. $5^3 =$

8.

	3	5	8
x			3

9. $72 \div 6 =$

10. Round 48015 to the nearest ten thousand.

21 TEST

1. $690 + 14 =$ ☐

2. $601 - 11 =$ ☐

3. $\frac{1}{10} + \frac{3}{10} =$ ☐

4. $2000 - 450 =$ ☐

5.
$$\begin{array}{r} 9\,7\,5\,6\,4 \\ +\ 5\,8\,0\,9\,8 \\ \hline \\ \hline \end{array}$$

6.
$$\begin{array}{r} 3\,4\,6\,7\,5 \\ -\ 1\,7\,3\,3\,7 \\ \hline \\ \hline \end{array}$$

7. $10^3 =$ ☐

8.
$$\begin{array}{r} 4\,6\,9 \\ \times\ \ \ \ 3 \\ \hline \\ \hline \end{array}$$

9. $54 \div 6 =$ ☐

10. Round 53987 to the nearest ten thousand. ☐

"I expect you know what 10^3 means!"

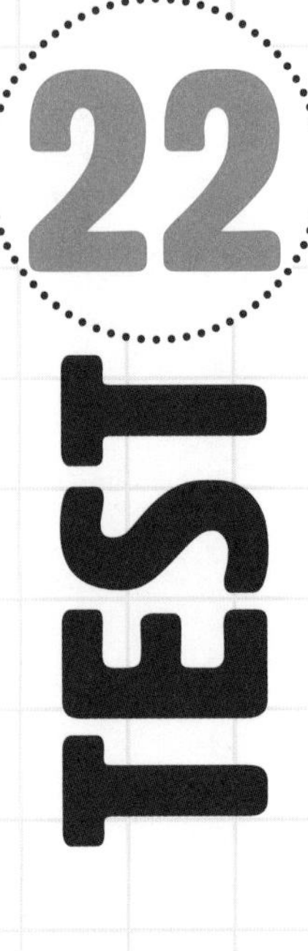

1. 190 + 15 =

2. 703 – 13 =

3. $\frac{3}{10} + \frac{3}{10} =$

4. 2000 – 650 =

5.

	4	7	8
	1	9	2
+		2	7

6.

	3	0	0	0	0
–	1	6	0	0	0

7. Change $4\frac{1}{2}$ to an improper fraction.

8.

	3	7	8
x			4

9. 66 ÷ 6 =

10. Round 98000 to the nearest ten thousand.

"In an improper fraction, the number at the top is bigger than the number at the bottom."

Well Done
Excellent
Great Work
Fantastic
FAB
!
?
Good Job
Keep It Up
Magnificent
Brilliant Work
SUPER
Well Done
Excellent
Great Work
Fantastic
FAB
!
?
Good Job
Keep It Up
Magnificent
Brilliant Work
SUPER
Well Done
Excellent
Great Work
Fantastic
FAB
!
?
Good Job
Keep It Up
Magnificent
Brilliant Work
SUPER
Well Done
Excellent
Great Work
Fantastic
FAB

Well Done
Excellent
Great Work
Fantastic
FAB
Good Job
Keep It Up
Magnificent
Brilliant Work
SUPER
Well Done
Excellent
Great Work
Fantastic
FAB
Good Job
Keep It Up
Magnificent
Brilliant Work
SUPER
Well Done
Excellent
Great Work
Fantastic
FAB
Good Job
Keep It Up
Magnificent
Brilliant Work
SUPER
Well Done
Excellent
Great Work
Fantastic
FAB

1. $890 + 19 =$ ☐

6.
```
   3 0 0 0 0
 − 2 3 4 5 6
```

2. $407 - 17 =$ ☐

7. Change $2\frac{1}{2}$ to an improper fraction. ☐

3. $\frac{5}{10} + \frac{3}{10} =$ ☐

8.
```
   4 6 9
 x     4
```

4. $2000 - 870 =$ ☐

9. $42 \div 6 =$ ☐

5.
```
   6 4 5
   2 3 6
 +   8 5
```

10. Round 236402 to the nearest ten thousand. ☐

To change a mixed number into an improper fraction, multiply the whole number by the denominator and add the result to the numerator."

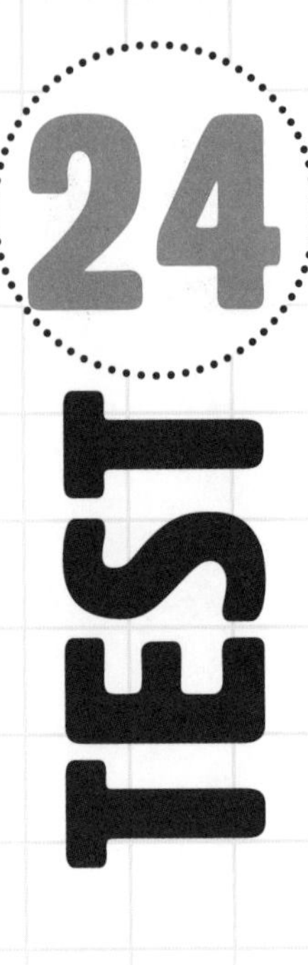

1. 290 + 16 =

2. 905 – 15 =

3. $\frac{7}{10} + \frac{1}{10} =$

4. 2000 – 643 =

5.

$$\begin{array}{r} 379 \\ 268 \\ +\quad 79 \\ \hline \\ \hline \end{array}$$

6.

$$\begin{array}{r} 40000 \\ -\ 14709 \\ \hline \\ \hline \end{array}$$

7. Change $3\frac{1}{2}$ to an improper fraction.

8.

$$\begin{array}{r} 379 \\ \times\quad 5 \\ \hline \\ \hline \end{array}$$

9. 36 ÷ 6 =

10. Round 379528 to the nearest ten thousand.

"Remember that the top part of a fraction is called the numerator."

25 TEST

1. $390 + 20 =$ ☐

2. $706 - 16 =$ ☐

3. $\frac{4}{10} + \frac{1}{10} =$ ☐

4. $5000 - 250 =$ ☐

5.

$$\begin{array}{r} 748 \\ 456 \\ +\quad 83 \\ \hline \\ \hline \end{array}$$

6.

$$\begin{array}{r} 60000 \\ -\ 23765 \\ \hline \\ \hline \end{array}$$

7. Change $5\frac{1}{2}$ to an improper fraction. ☐

8.

$$\begin{array}{r} 465 \\ \times\quad 5 \\ \hline \\ \hline \end{array}$$

9. $24 \div 6 =$ ☐

10. Round 379528 to the nearest hundred thousand. ☐

"Remember that the bottom part of a fraction is called the denominator."

26 TEST

1. 480 + 50 =

2. 706 – 26 =

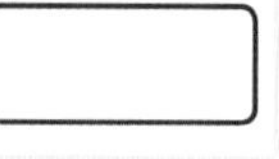

3. $\frac{3}{10} + \frac{7}{10} =$

4. 5000 – 1500 =

5.

	8	6	9
		5	8
+	9	1	4

6.

	5	8	9	3	7
–	3	2	7	1	4

7. Change $1\frac{1}{4}$ to an improper fraction.

8.

	7	3	8
x			6

9. 340 ÷ 10 =

10. Round 576239 to the nearest hundred thousand.

"Remember that in your answer to question 7, the numerator must be larger than the denominator."

TOTAL SCORE

TEST 27

1. $870 + 50 =$ ☐

2. $804 - 34 =$ ☐

3. $\frac{3}{10} + \frac{5}{10} =$ ☐

4. $5000 - 1450 =$ ☐

5.
$$\begin{array}{rrrr} & 7 & 6 & 3 \\ & & 8 & 8 \\ + & 4 & 5 & 6 \\ \hline \end{array}$$

6.
$$\begin{array}{rrrrrr} & 4 & 7 & 8 & 9 & 0 \\ - & 1 & 6 & 7 & 5 & 4 \\ \hline \end{array}$$

7. Change $2\frac{1}{4}$ to an improper fraction. ☐

8.
$$\begin{array}{rrrr} & 5 & 4 & 9 \\ \times & & & 6 \\ \hline \end{array}$$

9. $680 \div 10 =$ ☐

10. Round 649842 to the nearest hundred thousand. ☐

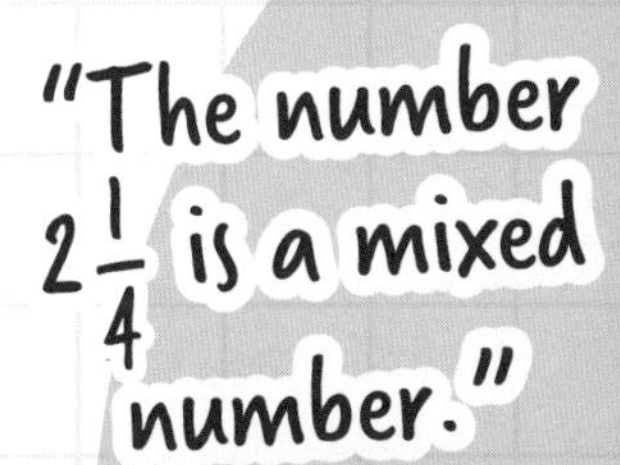

TEST 28

1. $680 + 70 =$ ☐

2. $907 - 47 =$ ☐

3. $\frac{7}{10} + \frac{7}{10} =$ ☐

4. $5000 - 2670 =$ ☐

5.
$$\begin{array}{r} 698 \\ 234 \\ +\ 379 \\ \hline \end{array}$$

6.
$$\begin{array}{r} 76017 \\ -\ 23471 \\ \hline \end{array}$$

7. Change $3\frac{1}{4}$ to an improper fraction. ☐

8.
$$\begin{array}{r} 264 \\ \times\ 7 \\ \hline \end{array}$$

9. $746 \div 10 =$ ☐

10. Round 712923 to the nearest hundred thousand. ☐

"The numerator of an improper fraction is larger than its denominator."

TEST

1. 570 + 80 =

2. 804 − 64 =

3. $\frac{7}{10} + \frac{9}{10} =$

4. 5000 − 3450 =

5.
```
    4 6 7
    5 2 9
+   7 3 4
```

6.
```
   8 9 0 1 7
−  3 5 2 6 8
```

7. Change $4\frac{1}{4}$ to an improper fraction.

8.
```
   9 7 3
x      7
```

9. 418 ÷ 10 =

10. Round 6.7 to the nearest whole number.

"In the number 6.7, the digit 7 is in the tenths column."

TOTAL SCORE

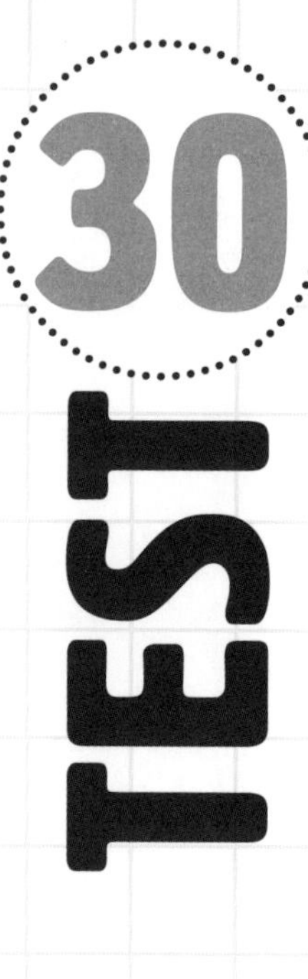

1. 460 + 90 = 

2. 307 − 77 =

3. $\frac{1}{5} + \frac{3}{5} =$

4. 5000 − 4876 =

5.

$$\begin{array}{r} 2345 \\ 678 \\ +\ 910 \\ \hline \end{array}$$

6.

$$\begin{array}{r} 146738 \\ -\ 56982 \\ \hline \end{array}$$

7. Change $1\frac{1}{4}$ to an improper fraction.

8.

$$\begin{array}{r} 468 \\ \times\ 8 \\ \hline \end{array}$$

9. 509 ÷ 10 =

10. Round 8.4 to the nearest whole number.

"When you add two fractions with the same denominator, only the numerator changes."

TEST 31

1. $780 + 60 =$ ☐

2. $806 - 56 =$ ☐

3. $\frac{2}{5} + \frac{3}{5} =$ ☐

4. $\frac{3}{4} - \frac{1}{4} =$ ☐

5.
$$\begin{array}{r} 3785 \\ 897 \\ +\ 356 \\ \hline \end{array}$$

6.
$$\begin{array}{r} 345981 \\ -\ 134278 \\ \hline \end{array}$$

7. Change $2\frac{3}{4}$ to an improper fraction. ☐

8.
$$\begin{array}{r} 739 \\ \times\ 8 \\ \hline \end{array}$$

9. $2\overline{)642}$

10. Round 12.9 to the nearest whole number. ☐

"Question 9 will test your short division skills."

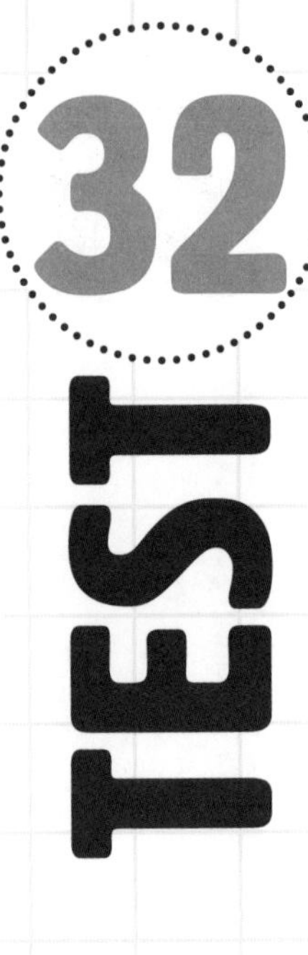

1. Double 12 =

2. $\frac{1}{2}$ x 18 =

3. $\frac{4}{5} - \frac{1}{5}$ =

4. $1\frac{1}{4} + \frac{1}{4}$ =

5.
```
    4 6 5
    3 1 6
+     2 4.7
```

6.
```
  4 2.0
- 2 1.6
```

7. Change $2\frac{3}{5}$ to an improper fraction.

8.
```
  4 6 2
x   2 3
```

9. 3) 5 9 1

10. 1 – 0.7 =

"In question 5, look which column the tenths are in."

TEST 33

1. Double 13 =

2. $\frac{1}{2}$ x 16 =

3. $\frac{1}{2} - \frac{1}{4}$ =

4. $1\frac{1}{4} + 1\frac{1}{4}$ =

5.
```
    3 2 7
    2 6 8
+     4 8 . 9
```

6.
```
  5 7 . 0
- 1 7 . 7
```

7. Change $\frac{7}{4}$ to a mixed number.

8.
```
  6 7 9
x   4 8
```

9. 4) 9 3 6

10. 1 – 0.4 =

REWARD STICKER!

"In question 6, look which column the tenths are in."

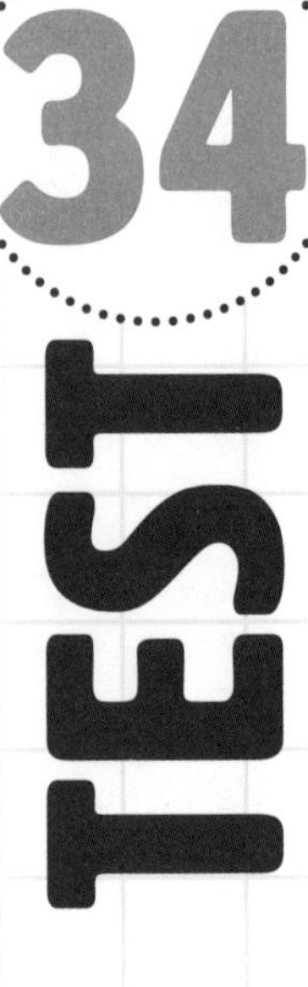

1.  Double 14 = 

2. $\frac{1}{2}$ x 22 =

3. $\frac{1}{2} + \frac{3}{4}$ = 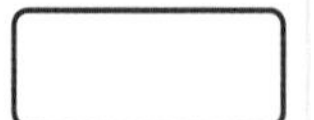

4. $2\frac{1}{4} + 1\frac{1}{4}$ =

5.
$$\begin{array}{r} 682 \\ 479.5 \\ +\ 126.8 \\ \hline \\ \hline \end{array}$$

6.
$$\begin{array}{r} 84.0 \\ -\ 26.9 \\ \hline \\ \hline \end{array}$$

7. Change $\frac{10}{3}$ to a mixed number. 

8.
$$\begin{array}{r} 1542 \\ \times\ \ 37 \\ \hline \\ \hline \\ \hline \end{array}$$

9. $7 \overline{)679}$

10. 1 – 0.2 =

"The fraction $\frac{10}{3}$ is called an improper fraction."

TEST 35

1. Double 18 = ☐

2. $\frac{1}{2} \times 48 =$ ☐

3. $3\frac{1}{2} + \frac{3}{4} =$ ☐

4. $4 - 1\frac{1}{4} =$ ☐

5. 

$$\begin{array}{r} 842.9 \\ 358 \\ +\ 273.8 \\ \hline \\ \hline \end{array}$$

6. $$\begin{array}{r} 96.0 \\ -\ 38.4 \\ \hline \\ \hline \end{array}$$

7. Change $\frac{12}{5}$ to a mixed number. ☐

8. $$\begin{array}{r} 3468 \\ \times\ \ \ 78 \\ \hline \\ \hline \\ \hline \end{array}$$

9. $8 \overline{)\,3456}$

10. $1 - 0.75 =$ ☐

"The fraction $\frac{12}{5}$ has a numerator that is bigger than its denominator."

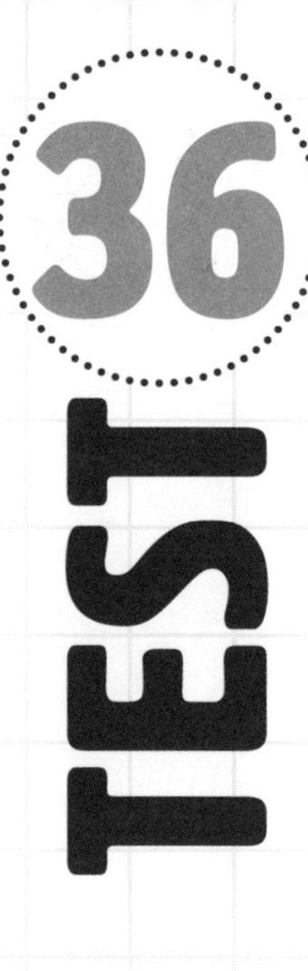

1. Double 21 =

2. $\frac{1}{2}$ x 50 =

3. $5\frac{1}{2} + \frac{3}{4}$ =

4. $7 - 2\frac{1}{4}$ =

5. Change $\frac{15}{4}$ to a mixed number.

6. 1 – 0.82 =

Set these questions out appropriately and fill in your answers:

7. 714.3 + 298.8 + 188

8. 78 – 26.7

9. 5271 x 96

10. 2982 ÷ 6

"Can you use the correct long addition, subtraction, multiplication and division methods for questions 7 to 10?"

TOTAL SCORE

TEST 37

1. Double 25 =

2. 50% of 40 =

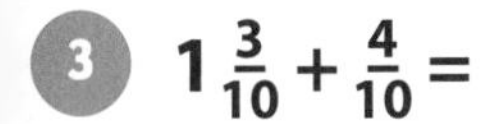

3. $1\frac{3}{10} + \frac{4}{10} =$

4. $8 - 3\frac{3}{10} =$

5. Change $\frac{10}{4}$ to a mixed number.

6. 4 – 0.76 =

Set these questions out appropriately and fill in your answers:

7. 369 + 485.7 + 69

8. 100 – 24.8

9. 12642 x 37

10. 5929 ÷ 7

"Did you know that 50% is the same as $\frac{1}{2}$?"

TEST 38

1. 37 x 10 =

2. 4.2 x 10 =

3. 1.6 + 1.2 =

4. 7 – 2.4 =

5. Change $\frac{1}{2}$ to a decimal.

6. 3 – 0.25 =

Set these questions out appropriately and fill in your answers:

7. 2468 + 397.5 + 248.5

8. 82 – 39.4

9. 15463 x 58

10. 2142 ÷ 9

"Are you getting faster?"

39

1. **216 x 10 =** ☐

2. **16.8 x 10 =** ☐

3. **4.7 + 2.5 =** ☐

4. **10 – 3.6 =** ☐

5. **Change $\frac{1}{2}$ to a decimal.** ☐

6. **4.7 x 100 =** ☐

Set these questions out appropriately and fill in your answers:

7. **307.4 + 1245 + 18.8**

8. **91 – 46.7**

9. **23964 x 37**

10. **6170 ÷ 5**

"Can you see what happens when you multiply by 10?"

40 TEST

1. 32748 x 10 =

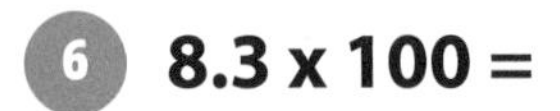

6. 8.3 x 100 =

2. 23.7 x 10 =

Set these questions out appropriately and fill in your answers:

7. 624 + 3798.6 + 48.4

3. 6.9 + 6.9 =

8. 235 – 58.9

4. 10 – 1.9 =

9. 34198 x 42

5. Change $\frac{3}{4}$ to a decimal.

10. 8952 ÷ 3

"This is the last test. Complete it as quickly as you can!"

ANSWERS

1

1. $79 + 6 = 85$
2. $92 - 8 = 84$
3. $3725 + 200 = 3925$
4. $6559 - 300 = 6259$
5. $$\begin{array}{r} 6\;4\;8 \\ +\;3\;3\;1 \\ \hline 9\;7\;9 \\ \hline \end{array}$$
6. $$\begin{array}{r} 8\;9\;6 \\ -\;3\;4\;5 \\ \hline 5\;5\;1 \\ \hline \end{array}$$
7. $16 + 5 = 10 + 11$
8. $36 = 4 \times 9$
9. $54 \div 6 = 9$
10. 4650

2

1. $84 + 9 = 93$
2. $73 - 6 = 67$
3. $4695 + 700 = 5395$
4. $8748 - 600 = 8148$
5. $$\begin{array}{r} 5\;7\;2 \\ +\;2\;1\;8 \\ \hline 7\;9\;0 \\ \hline {\scriptstyle 1}\;\; \end{array}$$
6. $$\begin{array}{r} \overset{6}{\cancel{7}}\;\overset{14}{\cancel{5}}\;{}^{1}4 \\ -\;4\;7\;7 \\ \hline 2\;7\;7 \\ \hline \end{array}$$
7. $27 + 6 = 10 + 23$
8. $48 = 4 \times 12$
9. $72 \div 8 = 9$
10. 5110

3

1. $123 + 8 = 131$
2. $144 - 6 = 138$
3. $5237 + 800 = 6037$
4. $9124 - 1000 = 8124$
5. $$\begin{array}{r} 8\;5\;9 \\ +\;3\;6\;7 \\ \hline 1\;2\;2\;6 \\ \hline {\scriptstyle 1}\;{\scriptstyle 1}\;\; \end{array}$$
6. $$\begin{array}{r} \overset{8}{\cancel{9}}\;{}^{1}4\;2 \\ -\;3\;8\;1 \\ \hline 5\;6\;1 \\ \hline \end{array}$$
7. $15 + 8 = 10 + 13$
8. $32 = 4 \times 8$
9. $96 \div 8 = 12$
10. 18640

4

1. $144 + 8 = 152$
2. $183 - 6 = 177$
3. $6192 + 900 = 7092$
4. $8431 - 2000 = 6431$
5. $$\begin{array}{r} 9\;7\;8 \\ +\;2\;9\;5 \\ \hline 1\;2\;7\;3 \\ \hline {\scriptstyle 1}\;{\scriptstyle 1}\;\; \end{array}$$
6. $$\begin{array}{r} 8\;7\;3 \\ -\;2\;4\;2 \\ \hline 6\;3\;1 \\ \hline \end{array}$$
7. $17 + 8 = 9 + 16$
8. $35 = 5 \times 7$
9. $64 \div 8 = 8$
10. 25600

5

1. $175 + 8 = 183$
2. $195 - 6 = 189$
3. $5734 + 800 = 6534$
4. $6274 - 800 = 5474$
5. $$\begin{array}{r} 7\;3\;9 \\ +\;4\;8\;8 \\ \hline 1\;2\;2\;7 \\ \hline {\scriptstyle 1}\;{\scriptstyle 1}\;\; \end{array}$$
6. $$\begin{array}{r} \overset{8}{\cancel{9}}\;{}^{1}\overset{9}{\cancel{0}}\;{}^{1}0 \\ -\;3\;5\;7 \\ \hline 5\;4\;3 \\ \hline \end{array}$$
7. $16 + 9 = 7 + 18$
8. $56 = 8 \times 7$
9. $40 \div 8 = 5$
10. 40020

6

1. $472 + 8 = 480$
2. $256 - 6 = 250$
3. $6935 + 200 = 7135$
4. $8427 - 600 = 7827$
5. $$\begin{array}{r} 1\;6\;4\;3 \\ +\;2\;9\;7 \\ \hline 1\;9\;4\;0 \\ \hline {\scriptstyle 1}\;{\scriptstyle 1}\;\; \end{array}$$
6. $$\begin{array}{r} 1\;5\;\overset{5}{\cancel{6}}\;{}^{1}0 \\ -\;4\;4\;8 \\ \hline 1\;1\;1\;2 \\ \hline \end{array}$$
7. $4^2 = 16$
8. $$\begin{array}{r} 4\;3 \\ \times\;\;\;3 \\ \hline 1\;2\;9 \\ \hline \end{array}$$
9. $108 \div 9 = 12$
10. 6500

7

1. $742 + 8 = 750$
2. $571 - 6 = 565$
3. $8493 + 600 = 9093$
4. $9397 - 700 = 8697$
5. $$\begin{array}{r} 5\;4\;7\;2 \\ +\;4\;7\;8 \\ \hline 5\;9\;5\;0 \\ \hline {\scriptstyle 1}\;{\scriptstyle 1}\;\; \end{array}$$
6. $$\begin{array}{r} 1\;\overset{5}{\cancel{6}}\;{}^{1}\overset{9}{\cancel{0}}\;{}^{1}0 \\ -\;5\;1\;2 \\ \hline 1\;0\;8\;8 \\ \hline \end{array}$$
7. $5^2 = 25$
8. $$\begin{array}{r} 2\;9 \\ \times\;\;\;3 \\ \hline 8\;7 \\ \hline {\scriptstyle 2}\;\; \end{array}$$
9. $81 \div 9 = 9$
10. 3500

8

1. $361 + 9 = 370$
2. $493 - 7 = 486$
3. $9904 + 700 = 10604$
4. $1000 - 250 = 750$
5. $$\begin{array}{r} 6\;3\;4\;2 \\ +\;1\;5\;7\;9 \\ \hline 7\;9\;2\;1 \\ \hline {\scriptstyle 1}\;{\scriptstyle 1}\;\; \end{array}$$
6. $$\begin{array}{r} 2\;\overset{7}{\cancel{8}}\;\overset{13}{\cancel{4}}\;{}^{1}2 \\ -\;1\;6\;9\;7 \\ \hline 1\;1\;4\;5 \\ \hline \end{array}$$
7. $6^2 = 36$
8. $$\begin{array}{r} 4\;8 \\ \times\;\;\;4 \\ \hline 1\;9\;2 \\ \hline {\scriptstyle 3}\;\; \end{array}$$
9. $63 \div 9 = 7$
10. 12300

9

1. $412 + 9 = 421$
2. $684 - 7 = 677$
3. $7777 + 700 = 8477$
4. $1000 - 418 = 582$
5. $$\begin{array}{r} 8\,9\,3\,5 \\ +\ 2\,7\,8\,4 \\ \hline 1\,1\,7\,1\,9 \\ \scriptstyle 1\ 1\ \ \ \ \end{array}$$
6. $$\begin{array}{r} \scriptstyle 5\ 9\ 12\ 1 \\ 6\,0\,3\,2 \\ -\ 2\,7\,9\,4 \\ \hline 3\,2\,3\,8 \end{array}$$
7. $7^2 = 49$
8. $$\begin{array}{r} 5\,6 \\ \times\ \ 4 \\ \hline 2\,2\,4 \\ \scriptstyle 2\ \ \ \end{array}$$
9. $54 \div 9 = 6$
10. 17700

10

1. $533 + 9 = 542$
2. $755 - 7 = 748$
3. $8564 + 600 = 9164$
4. $1000 - 193 = 807$
5. $$\begin{array}{r} 7\,6\,2\,9 \\ +\ 3\,5\,8\,2 \\ \hline 1\,1\,2\,1\,1 \\ \scriptstyle 1\ 1\ 1\ \ \end{array}$$
6. $$\begin{array}{r} \scriptstyle 4\ 1\ \ \ \ \ \\ 5\,1\,3\,6 \\ -\ 3\,9\,2\,4 \\ \hline 1\,2\,1\,2 \end{array}$$
7. $8^2 = 64$
8. $$\begin{array}{r} 7\,8 \\ \times\ \ 4 \\ \hline 3\,1\,2 \\ \scriptstyle 3\ \ \ \end{array}$$
9. $45 \div 9 = 5$
10. 47700

11

1. $624 + 9 = 633$
2. $966 - 7 = 959$
3. $5920 + 700 = 6620$
4. $1000 - 623 = 377$
5. $$\begin{array}{r} 9\,2\,7\,8 \\ +\ 8\,0\,4\,7 \\ \hline 1\,7\,3\,2\,5 \\ \scriptstyle 1\ 1\ \ \end{array}$$
6. $$\begin{array}{r} \scriptstyle 6\ 12\ 13\ 1 \\ 7\,3\,4\,2 \\ -\ 5\,8\,4\,7 \\ \hline 1\,4\,9\,5 \end{array}$$
7. $9^2 = 81$
8. $$\begin{array}{r} 8\,6 \\ \times\ \ 4 \\ \hline 3\,4\,4 \\ \scriptstyle 2\ \ \ \end{array}$$
9. $36 \div 9 = 4$
10. 207200

12

1. $105 + 9 = 114$
2. $842 - 12 = 830$
3. $12347 + 500 = 12847$
4. $1000 - 212 = 788$
5. $$\begin{array}{r} 1\,4\,6\,7\,8 \\ +\ \ \ 2\,9\,4\,7 \\ \hline 1\,7\,6\,2\,5 \\ \scriptstyle 1\ 1\ 1\ \ \end{array}$$
6. $$\begin{array}{r} \scriptstyle 7\ 9\ 10\ 1 \\ 8\,0\,1\,0 \\ -\ 3\,6\,2\,9 \\ \hline 4\,3\,8\,1 \end{array}$$
7. $1^2 = 1$
8. $$\begin{array}{r} 4\,8 \\ \times\ \ 7 \\ \hline 3\,3\,6 \\ \scriptstyle 5\ \ \ \end{array}$$
9. $32 \div 8 = 4$
10. 207000

13

1. $666 + 9 = 675$
2. $674 - 14 = 660$
3. $15384 + 900 = 16284$
4. $1000 - 622 = 378$
5. $$\begin{array}{r} 3\,6\,7\,4\,3 \\ +\ \ \ 5\,6\,0\,9 \\ \hline 4\,2\,3\,5\,2 \\ \scriptstyle 1\ 1\ \ \ 1\ \ \end{array}$$
6. $$\begin{array}{r} \scriptstyle 8\ 9\ 9\ 1 \\ 9\,0\,0\,0 \\ -\ 4\,8\,4\,2 \\ \hline 4\,1\,5\,8 \end{array}$$
7. $10^2 = 100$
8. $$\begin{array}{r} 5\,3 \\ \times\ \ 7 \\ \hline 3\,7\,1 \\ \scriptstyle 2\ \ \ \end{array}$$
9. $48 \div 8 = 6$
10. 345000

14

1. $437 + 9 = 446$
2. $839 - 19 = 820$
3. $23602 + 300 = 23902$
4. $1000 - 795 = 205$
5. $$\begin{array}{r} 4\,8\,3\,4\,9 \\ +\ \ \ 7\,5\,9\,9 \\ \hline 5\,5\,9\,4\,8 \\ \scriptstyle 1\ \ \ 1\ 1\ \ \end{array}$$
6. $$\begin{array}{r} \scriptstyle 7\ 9\ 9\ 1 \\ 8\,0\,0\,0 \\ -\ 3\,4\,2\,8 \\ \hline 4\,5\,7\,2 \end{array}$$
7. $11^2 = 121$
8. $$\begin{array}{r} 8\,9 \\ \times\ \ 7 \\ \hline 6\,2\,3 \\ \scriptstyle 6\ \ \ \end{array}$$
9. $56 \div 8 = 7$
10. 765000

15

1. $768 + 9 = 777$
2. $595 - 15 = 580$
3. $18798 + 600 = 19398$
4. $1000 - 47 = 953$
5. $$\begin{array}{r} 6\,7\,3\,4\,2 \\ +\ \ \ 8\,0\,9\,1 \\ \hline 7\,5\,4\,3\,3 \\ \scriptstyle 1\ \ \ 1\ \ \ \ \ \end{array}$$
6. $$\begin{array}{r} \scriptstyle 6\ 9\ 9\ 1 \\ 7\,0\,0\,0 \\ -\ 1\,7\,6\,4 \\ \hline 5\,2\,3\,6 \end{array}$$
7. $12^2 = 144$
8. $$\begin{array}{r} 6\,5 \\ \times\ \ 7 \\ \hline 4\,5\,5 \\ \scriptstyle 3\ \ \ \end{array}$$
9. $64 \div 8 = 8$
10. 301000

16

1. $999 + 9 = 1008$
2. $426 - 16 = 410$
3. $46729 + 200 = 46929$
4. $1000 - 675 = 325$
5. $$\begin{array}{r} 1\,6\,7\,8\,4 \\ +\ \ \ 9\,4\,7\,2 \\ \hline 2\,6\,2\,5\,6 \\ \scriptstyle 1\ 1\ 1\ \ \ \ \end{array}$$
6. $$\begin{array}{r} \scriptstyle 0\ 1\ \ \ \ \ \ \ \\ 1\,6\,7\,8\,4 \\ -\ \ \ 9\,4\,7\,2 \\ \hline 7\,3\,1\,2 \end{array}$$
7. $1^3 = 1$
8. $$\begin{array}{r} 2\,4\,6 \\ \times\ \ \ \ 2 \\ \hline 4\,9\,2 \\ \scriptstyle 1\ \ \ \end{array}$$
9. $96 \div 8 = 12$
10. 248000

17

1. 460 + 12 = 472
2. 818 − 18 = 800
3. $\frac{1}{5} + \frac{2}{5} = \frac{3}{5}$
4. 1000 − 319 = 681
5.
```
    4 7 3 4 1
+   1 7 0 6 3
  -----------
    6 4 4 0 4
    1   1
```
6.
```
    3 16  1
    4  7  2 9 4
−      8  5 6 3
  -------------
    3  8  7 3 1
```
7. $2^3 = 8$
8.
```
    3 6 7
x       2
  -------
    7 3 4
    1 1
```
9. 49 ÷ 7 = 7
10. 50000

18

1. 580 + 13 = 593
2. 647 − 17 = 630
3. $\frac{1}{6} + \frac{1}{6} = \frac{2}{6}$ or $\frac{1}{3}$
4. 1000 − 150 = 850
5.
```
    7 8 0 1 9
+   1 5 2 3 4
  -----------
    9 3 2 5 3
    1     1
```
6.
```
          7 1
    6 3 7 8 2
−   2 3 6 1 5
  -----------
    4 0 1 6 7
```
7. $3^3 = 27$
8.
```
    4 7 9
x       2
  -------
    9 5 8
    1 1
```
9. 63 ÷ 7 = 9
10. 80000

19

1. 620 + 19 = 639
2. 934 − 14 = 920
3. $\frac{1}{8} + \frac{3}{8} = \frac{4}{8}$ or $\frac{1}{2}$
4. 1000 − 742 = 258
5.
```
    4 7 2 9 5
+   2 3 9 7 6
  -----------
    7 1 2 7 1
    1 1 1 1
```
6.
```
    7 13 1
    8  4 3 2 8
−   3  5 6 1 3
  ------------
    4  8 7 1 5
```
7. $4^3 = 64$
8.
```
      8 5 9
x         2
  ---------
    1 7 1 8
      1 1
```
9. 84 ÷ 7 = 12
10. 70000

20

1. 790 + 11 = 801
2. 467 − 17 = 450
3. $\frac{1}{8} + \frac{5}{8} = \frac{6}{8}$ or $\frac{3}{4}$
4. 2000 − 750 = 1250
5.
```
      8 9 3 2 6
+     3 7 4 5 6
  -------------
    1 2 6 7 8 2
      1     1
```
6.
```
    8 1 6 12 1
    9 2 7  3 4
−   8 7 6  3 9
  ------------
      5 0  9 5
```
7. $5^3 = 125$
8.
```
      3 5 8
x         3
  ---------
    1 0 7 4
      1 2
```
9. 72 ÷ 6 = 12
10. 50000

21

1. 690 + 14 = 704
2. 601 − 11 = 590
3. $\frac{1}{10} + \frac{3}{10} = \frac{4}{10}$ or $\frac{2}{5}$
4. 2000 − 450 = 1550
5.
```
      9 7 5 6 4
+     5 8 0 9 8
  -------------
    1 5 5 6 6 2
      1   1 1
```
6.
```
    2 1   6 1
    3 4 6 7 5
−   1 7 3 3 7
  -----------
    1 7 3 3 8
```
7. $10^3 = 1000$
8.
```
      4 6 9
x         3
  ---------
    1 4 0 7
      2 2
```
9. 54 ÷ 6 = 9
10. 50000

22

1. 190 + 15 = 205
2. 703 − 13 = 690
3. $\frac{3}{10} + \frac{3}{10} = \frac{6}{10}$ or $\frac{3}{5}$
4. 2000 − 650 = 1350
5.
```
    4 7 8
    1 9 2
+     2 7
  -------
    6 9 7
    1 1
```
6.
```
    2 1
    3 0 0 0 0
−   1 6 0 0 0
  -----------
    1 4 0 0 0
```
7. $\frac{9}{2}$
8.
```
      3 7 8
x         4
  ---------
    1 5 1 2
      3 3
```
9. 66 ÷ 6 = 11
10. 100000

23

1. 890 + 19 = 909
2. 407 − 17 = 390
3. $\frac{5}{10} + \frac{3}{10} = \frac{8}{10}$ or $\frac{4}{5}$
4. 2000 − 870 = 1130
5.
```
    6 4 5
    2 3 6
+     8 5
  -------
    9 6 6
    1 1
```
6.
```
    2 9 9 9 1
    3 0 0 0 0
−   2 3 4 5 6
  -----------
      6 5 4 4
```
7. $\frac{5}{2}$
8.
```
      4 6 9
x         4
  ---------
    1 8 7 6
      2 3
```
9. 42 ÷ 6 = 7
10. 240000

24

1. 290 + 16 = 306
2. 905 − 15 = 890
3. $\frac{7}{10} + \frac{1}{10} = \frac{8}{10}$ or $\frac{4}{5}$
4. 2000 − 643 = 1357
5.
```
    3 7 9
    2 6 8
+     7 9
  -------
    7 2 6
    2 2
```
6.
```
    3 9 9 9 1
    4 0 0 0 0
−   1 4 7 0 9
  -----------
    2 5 2 9 1
```
7. $\frac{7}{2}$
8.
```
      3 7 9
x         5
  ---------
    1 8 9 5
      3 4
```
9. 36 ÷ 6 = 6
10. 380000

25

1. 390 + 20 = 410
2. 706 – 16 = 690
3. $\frac{4}{10}+\frac{1}{10}=\frac{5}{10}$ or $\frac{1}{2}$
4. 5000 – 250 = 4750
5. $$\begin{array}{r} 748 \\ 456 \\ +\ \ 83 \\ \hline 1287 \\ \hline {}_{1\,1\ } \end{array}$$
6. $$\begin{array}{r} 60000 \\ -\ 23765 \\ \hline 36235 \\ \hline \end{array}$$
7. $\frac{11}{2}$
8. $$\begin{array}{r} 465 \\ \times\ \ \ 5 \\ \hline 2325 \\ \hline {}_{3\,2\ } \end{array}$$
9. 24 ÷ 6 = 4
10. 400000

26

1. 480 + 50 = 530
2. 706 – 26 = 680
3. $\frac{3}{10}+\frac{7}{10}=1$
4. 5000 – 1500 = 3500
5. $$\begin{array}{r} 869 \\ 58 \\ +\ 914 \\ \hline 1841 \\ \hline {}_{1\,2\ } \end{array}$$
6. $$\begin{array}{r} 58937 \\ -\ 32714 \\ \hline 26223 \\ \hline \end{array}$$
7. $\frac{5}{4}$
8. $$\begin{array}{r} 738 \\ \times\ \ \ 6 \\ \hline 4428 \\ \hline {}_{2\,4\ } \end{array}$$
9. 340 ÷ 10 = 34
10. 600000

27

1. 870 + 50 = 920
2. 804 – 34 = 770
3. $\frac{3}{10}+\frac{5}{10}=\frac{8}{10}$ or $\frac{4}{5}$
4. 5000 – 1450 = 3550
5. $$\begin{array}{r} 763 \\ 88 \\ +\ 456 \\ \hline 1307 \\ \hline {}_{2\,1\ } \end{array}$$
6. $$\begin{array}{r} 47890 \\ -\ 16754 \\ \hline 31136 \\ \hline \end{array}$$
7. $\frac{9}{4}$
8. $$\begin{array}{r} 549 \\ \times\ \ \ 6 \\ \hline 3294 \\ \hline {}_{2\,5\ } \end{array}$$
9. 680 ÷ 10 = 68
10. 600000

28

1. 680 + 70 = 750
2. 907 – 47 = 860
3. $\frac{7}{10}+\frac{7}{10}=1\frac{4}{10}$
4. 5000 – 2670 = 2330
5. $$\begin{array}{r} 698 \\ 234 \\ +\ 379 \\ \hline 1311 \\ \hline {}_{2\,2\ } \end{array}$$
6. $$\begin{array}{r} 76017 \\ -\ 23471 \\ \hline 52546 \\ \hline \end{array}$$
7. $\frac{13}{4}$
8. $$\begin{array}{r} 264 \\ \times\ \ \ 7 \\ \hline 1848 \\ \hline {}_{4\,2\ } \end{array}$$
9. 746 ÷ 10 = 74.6
10. 700000

29

1. 570 + 80 = 650
2. 804 – 64 = 740
3. $\frac{7}{10}+\frac{9}{10}=1\frac{6}{10}$ or $1\frac{3}{5}$
4. 5000 – 3450 = 1550
5. $$\begin{array}{r} 467 \\ 529 \\ +\ 734 \\ \hline 1730 \\ \hline {}_{1\,2\ } \end{array}$$
6. $$\begin{array}{r} 89017 \\ -\ 35268 \\ \hline 53749 \\ \hline \end{array}$$
7. $\frac{17}{4}$
8. $$\begin{array}{r} 973 \\ \times\ \ \ 7 \\ \hline 6811 \\ \hline {}_{5\,2\ } \end{array}$$
9. 418 ÷ 10 = 41.8
10. 7

30

1. 460 + 90 = 550
2. 307 – 77 = 230
3. $\frac{1}{5}+\frac{3}{5}=\frac{4}{5}$
4. 5000 – 4876 = 124
5. $$\begin{array}{r} 2345 \\ 678 \\ +\ 910 \\ \hline 3933 \\ \hline {}_{1\,1\,1\ } \end{array}$$
6. $$\begin{array}{r} 146738 \\ -\ 56982 \\ \hline 89756 \\ \hline \end{array}$$
7. $\frac{5}{4}$
8. $$\begin{array}{r} 468 \\ \times\ \ \ 8 \\ \hline 3744 \\ \hline {}_{5\,6\ } \end{array}$$
9. 509 ÷ 10 = 50.9
10. 8

31

1. 780 + 60 = 840
2. 806 – 56 = 750
3. $\frac{2}{5}+\frac{3}{5}=1$
4. $\frac{3}{4}-\frac{1}{4}=\frac{2}{4}$ or $\frac{1}{2}$
5. $$\begin{array}{r} 3785 \\ 897 \\ +\ 356 \\ \hline 5038 \\ \hline {}_{2\,2\,1\ } \end{array}$$
6. $$\begin{array}{r} 345981 \\ -\ 134278 \\ \hline 211703 \\ \hline \end{array}$$
7. $\frac{11}{4}$
8. $$\begin{array}{r} 739 \\ \times\ \ \ 8 \\ \hline 5912 \\ \hline {}_{3\,7\ } \end{array}$$
9. $$\begin{array}{r} 321 \\ 2\overline{)642} \end{array}$$
10. 13

32

1. Double 12 = 24
2. $\frac{1}{2}$ x 18 = 9
3. $\frac{4}{5}-\frac{1}{5}=\frac{3}{5}$
4. $1\frac{1}{4}+\frac{1}{4}=1\frac{2}{4}$ or $1\frac{1}{2}$
5. $$\begin{array}{r} 465 \\ 316 \\ +\ 24.7 \\ \hline 805.7 \\ \hline \end{array}$$
6. $$\begin{array}{r} 42.0 \\ -\ 21.6 \\ \hline 20.4 \\ \hline \end{array}$$
7. $\frac{13}{5}$
8. $$\begin{array}{r} 462 \\ \times\ \ 23 \\ \hline 1386 \\ 9240 \\ \hline 10626 \\ \hline \end{array}$$
9. $$\begin{array}{r} 197 \\ 3\overline{)591} \end{array}$$
10. 1 – 0.7 = 0.3

33

1. Double 13 = 26
2. $\frac{1}{2} \times 16 = 8$
3. $\frac{1}{2} + \frac{1}{4} = \frac{3}{4}$
4. $1\frac{1}{4} + 1\frac{1}{4} = 2\frac{2}{4}$ or $2\frac{1}{2}$
5. $327 + 268 + 48.9 = 643.9$
6. $57.0 - 17.7 = 39.3$
7. $1\frac{3}{4}$
8. 679×48: 5432; 27160; = 32592
9. $936 \div 4 = 234$
10. $1 - 0.4 = 0.6$

34

1. Double 14 = 28
2. $\frac{1}{2} \times 22 = 11$
3. $\frac{1}{2} + \frac{3}{4} = 1\frac{1}{4}$
4. $2\frac{1}{4} + 1\frac{1}{4} = 3\frac{2}{4}$ or $3\frac{1}{2}$
5. $682 + 479.5 + 126.8 = 1288.3$
6. $84.0 - 26.9 = 57.1$
7. $3\frac{1}{3}$
8. 1542×37: 10794; 46260; = 57054
9. $679 \div 7 = 97$
10. $1 - 0.2 = 0.8$

35

1. Double 18 = 36
2. $\frac{1}{2} \times 48 = 24$
3. $3\frac{1}{2} + \frac{3}{4} = 4\frac{1}{4}$
4. $4 - 1\frac{1}{4} = 2\frac{3}{4}$
5. $842.9 + 358 + 273.8 = 1474.7$
6. $96.0 - 38.4 = 57.6$
7. $2\frac{2}{5}$
8. 3468×78: 27744; 242760; = 270504
9. $3456 \div 8 = 432$
10. $1 - 0.75 = 0.25$

36

1. Double 21 = 42
2. $\frac{1}{2} \times 50 = 25$
3. $5\frac{1}{2} + \frac{3}{4} = 6\frac{1}{4}$
4. $7 - 2\frac{1}{4} = 4\frac{3}{4}$
5. $3\frac{3}{4}$
6. $1 - 0.82 = 0.18$
7. $714.3 + 298.8 + 188 = 1201.1$
8. $78.0 - 26.7 = 51.3$
9. 5271×96: 31626; 474390; = 506016
10. $2982 \div 6 = 497$

37

1. Double 25 = 50
2. 50% of 40 = 20
3. $1\frac{3}{10} + \frac{4}{10} = 1\frac{7}{10}$
4. $8 - 3\frac{3}{10} = 4\frac{7}{10}$
5. $2\frac{2}{4}$ or $2\frac{1}{2}$
6. $4 - 0.76 = 3.24$
7. $369 + 485.7 + 69 = 923.7$
8. $100.0 - 24.8 = 75.2$
9. 12642×37: 88494; 379260; = 467754
10. $5929 \div 7 = 847$

38

1. $37 \times 10 = 370$
2. $4.2 \times 10 = 42$
3. $1.6 + 1.2 = 2.8$
4. $7 - 2.4 = 4.6$
5. 0.5
6. $3 - 0.25 = 2.75$
7. $2468 + 397.5 + 248.5 = 3114.0$
8. $82.0 - 39.4 = 42.6$
9. 15463×58: 123704; 773150; = 896854
10. $2142 \div 9 = 238$

39

1. $216 \times 10 = 2160$
2. $16.8 \times 10 = 168$
3. $4.7 + 2.5 = 7.2$
4. $10 - 3.6 = 6.4$
5. 0.25
6. $4.7 \times 100 = 470$
7. $307.4 + 1245 + 18.8 = 1571.2$
8. $91.0 - 46.7 = 44.3$
9. 23964×37: 167748; 718920; = 886668
10. $6170 \div 5 = 1234$

40

1. $32748 \times 10 = 327480$
2. $23.7 \times 10 = 237$
3. $6.9 + 6.9 = 13.8$
4. $10 - 1.9 = 8.1$
5. 0.75
6. $8.3 \times 100 = 830$
7. $624 + 3798.6 + 48.4 = 4471.0$
8. $238.0 - 58.9 = 176.1$
9. 34198×42: 68396; 1367920; = 1436316
10. $8952 \div 3 = 2984$

CHART YOUR PROGRESS

Shade in the chart to record your score in each test.

SCORE

TEST

	1	2	3	4	5	6	7	8	9	10
1										
2										
3										
4										
5										
6										
7										
8										
9										
10										
11										
12										
13										
14										
15										
16										
17										
18										
19										
20										
21										
22										
23										
24										
25										
26										
27										
28										
29										
30										
31										
32										
33										
34										
35										
36										
37										
38										
39										
40										